JUDGE DREDD in the ★ CURSED EARTH

Pat Mills
Mike McMahon
Brian Bolland
★

INTRODUCTION

*T*he Cursed Earth **remains to this day one of the most ambitious** *Judge Dredd* **stories conceived. Comprising twenty five episodes and over 150 pages of artwork, which ran in Progs 61-85 of the weekly comic,** *2000 AD,* **it is all the more remarkable for the fact that only two artists – Mike McMahon (18 chapters) and Brian Bolland (7 chapters) – worked on it. The writing was handled by Pat Mills, creator and former editor of** *2000 AD,* **assisted by John Wagner on four chapters and Jack Adrian on two. The first half of** The Cursed Earth **contains three new pages drawn by Brian Bolland to provide visual continuity.**

The story concerns Judge Dredd, *2000 AD*'s most popular hero, and his vital mission to deliver a precious cargo of life-saving vaccine across the treacherous wastelands of the Cursed Earth to the plague-ridden inhabitants of Mega-City Two. Writer Pat Mills removed Dredd from his normal Mega-City One beat, which he considered to be more the scripting province of regular John Wagner, and gave Dredd two major protagonists, Spikes 'Harvey' Rotten and Tweak. Spikes was an anarchistic 'Johnny Rotten' style punk who hated the world and everything that Dredd stood for, and acted as both his companion and foil. Mills pulled Rotten from an earlier Dredd story *The Mega-City 5000* (Progs 41 & 42), Brian Bolland's first artwork on the series, and fleshed out his character, giving him a new, and more appropriate, visual appearance. Tweak was an 'original'. Mills had never felt happy writing Walter, Dredd's regular companion, but wanted a character that the readers could sympathise with and that could get beaten up, tortured and shot at – and still come out alive! When he spotted an incredible looking creature called a Tamundua (a Peruvian anteater) in an issue of *National Geographic* he knew he had the answer.

The other subsidiary characters – three judges and three war droids – came along as cannon fodder. Mills was so enthusiastic about disposing of his creations that he even named the first Cursed Earth casualty – Assistant Grand Judge Fodder! Even Dredd underwent character changes – from a relentless, macho city cop, who could only cope with the insanity of Mega-City One by being tougher and more ruthless than its inhabitants, to a fairer, more compassionate lawman whose treatment of the Cursed Earth mutants was both sympathetic and just.

The Cursed Earth lay between two giant Mega-Cities, represented by modern day New York State and California, which meant that Dredd's East to West route had to make geographical sense. This caused some problems. Mills had been determined to introduce a story concerning Mount Rushmore and the Presidents' heads as early as possible, but, having plotted it, he discovered the site was a lot further west than he'd hoped. He didn't want to change his story, so he changed America. He wrote in an extra paragraph explaining how Rushmore had been relocated to just outside Mega-City One on the premise that sightseers and tourists wouldn't have to travel so far to see it.

Chapters 11-25 of *The Cursed Earth* originally featured in Progs 71-85 of *2000 AD.* One page has been deleted (the opening page for the original Chapter 20, entitled 'The God Judge') which has condensed two chapters into one, and is now called 'Loser's Leap'; four complete chapters – two stories – have also been excised because they contain characters which were alleged infringement of trademark.

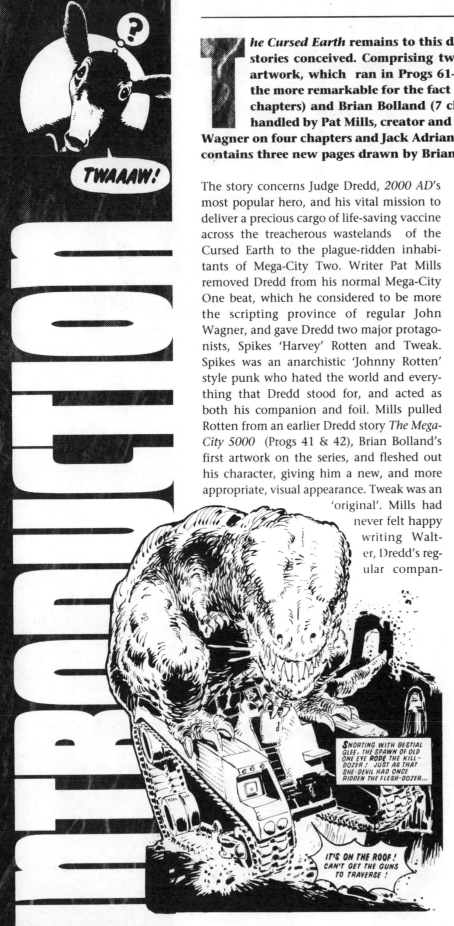

SNORTING WITH BESTIAL GLEE, THE SPAWN OF OLD ONE EYE *RODE* THE KILL-DOZER! JUST AS THAT SHE-DEVIL HAD ONCE RIDDEN THE FLESH-DOZER...

IT'S ON THE ROOF! CAN'T GET THE GUNS TO TRAVERSE!

THIS IS MADNESS. THERE'S NO *DEATH SENTENCE* FOR WORKING FOR THE WRONG HAMBURGER CHAIN.

MAYBE WHAR YU COME FROM, BOY, BUT OUT HERE WE GOT OUR OWN KIND OF LAW — *BURGER LAW!*

The first two chapters (the original Chapters 11 and 12), entitled 'Battle of the Burger Barons' and 'Burger Law' (Progs 71 and 72), written by John Wagner and drawn by Mike McMahon, involved Judge Dredd and Spikes 'Harvey' Rotten, the punk biker, in a war between two Burger Barons, descendants of original fast-food chain owners. Captured by the Marauders and taken back to MacDonald City to be force-fed on a diet of burgers and double thick shakes, they escape the sluggish burger-fed guards only to fall into the hands of the opposition, who mistake them for Marauders and want to string them up for working for the wrong hamburger chain. Rescue arrives at the last moment in the form of Judge Jack and the Land Raider and Dredd insists that the mission proceed immediately.

'Giants Aren't Gentlemen' and 'Soul Food' (Progs 77 and 78 – the original Chapters 17 and 18) were written by Jack

Adrian and drawn by Brian Bolland. In the midst of the Cursed Earth, Dredd and his crew come across a pre-atomic war agricultural research station run by a mad scientist, Dr Gibbon, who bears more than a passing resemblance to a well known Southern Fried Chicken magnate. Gibbon has been experimenting with the creation of artificial life from vegetable tissue and his research station is populated with a mixture of humans and weird freaks based on instantly recognisable characters of the 20th Century. After Dredd's capture and escape, a final battle takes place involving the freaks, and the eventual destruction of the research station.

The Cursed Earth contained some of the

NOT GOOD ENUFF, BOY. WE GOT STANDARDS O' *CLEANLINESS* TO MAINTAIN.

AAAAAGH!

THE GIANT TURNS... RACES AWAY WITHIN SECONDS, HE IS *LOST* TO SIGHT IN THE FOREST OF GRASS...

HA HA EVEN BETTER THAN MATCHSTICKS UNDER THE TOE-NAILS!

WE WERE WARNED OF WHAT WE MIGHT ENCOUNTER ON THIS MISSION, BUT SOME-ONE FORGOT TO MENTION *A HOMICIDAL 30-FOOT HIGH GREEN MAN!*

most violent and yet memorable moments in Dredd's history. Satanus and his fellow dinosaurs scored an incredibly high and bloody body-count in the second half of the book, although this seemed paltry compared to the count his mother, Old One Eye, achieved in 'Flesh', a dinosaur story that originally appeared in Progs 1–19 of *2000AD*; the main objective of 'Flesh' was to see how many people could fall into Old One Eye's gaping jaws each week. 'Bull' Cannon really showed what a tough guy he was by spending the last moments of his life wandering around with a dinosaur tooth stuck through his head. Tweak solicited sympathy and pathos during his implied vivisection in the hands of the human doctors who wanted to ascertain whether he was an intelligent alien life form or just a dumb animal. Mills' exciting and emotionally charged writing, coupled with McMahon's and Bolland's action-packed artwork, thrust the reader right into the heart of the story each week, creating feelings of horror, sympathy and excitement.

Because the first two pages, or 'spread', of each episode originally appeared in colour, they were needed at the printers two weeks before the rest of the story. Consequently, the remaining pages were not completed until later and, as they were often behind schedule, they did not always feature the credited artist or letterer. The missing credits in this book are Paul Bensberg's lettering of pages 32–36 in 'Loser's Leap' (Chapter 15); Dave Gibbons' inking and lettering of pages 44–48 in 'Tweak's Story' (Chapter 16); Steve Potter's lettering of pages 52–56 in 'Tweak's Story' (Chapter 17); and Tom Frame's lettering of pages 68–73 in 'Dredd's Last Stand' (Chapter 19).

The Cursed Earth represented a high point in Dredd's popularity with the readers, his highest ever votes coming from the Satanus stories. Judge Dredd has now made his mark in comic history, having won Eagle Awards – fandom's highest accolade – in many categories every year.

Nick Landau 1981/1982

WE ARE *ALL* HUNGRY IN DELIVERANCE. THAT CAN BE NO EXCUSE. I HEREBY SENTENCE YOU TO *DEATH* . . .

. . . TO BE EATEN ALIVE . . . *BY THE DEVIL'S LAPDOGS!*

I, THE LAWGIVER, HAVE SPOKEN!

THE COLLECTED JUDGE DREDD IN THE CURSED EARTH
ISBN 1 85286 406 0

Published by
Titan Books Ltd
42-44 Dolben St
London SE1 0UP

First published in *2000 AD* Progs 61-85. Compiled into two individual volumes by Titan Books as *The Cursed Earth* Volumes 1-2 (1981/2). This edition first published May 1994. This arrangement © Titan Books Ltd 1994. *Judge Dredd* © Fleetway Editions 1994.

Front cover illustration by Brian Bolland. Back cover illustration by Mike McMahon.

Printed in Singapore.

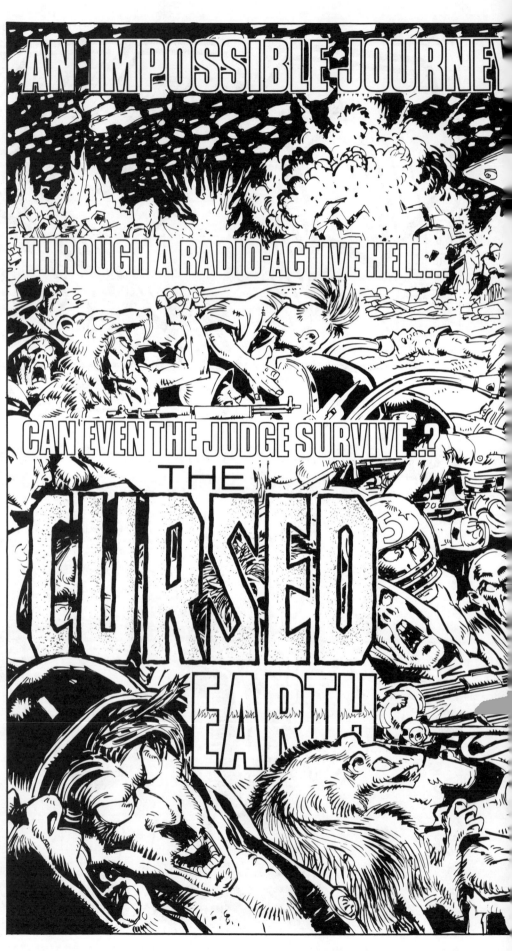

WE MUST PEEL THEM WITH THE KNIVES...

OH, MY GOD! THOSE POOR DEVILS...THE PLAGUE'S TURNED THEM INTO *CRAZY CANNIBALS!*

KILL! THIS FRUIT IS FRESH AND *READY FOR PICKING*...UGH!

EEEEEEGH!

GOT NO CHOICE... GOTTA **GUN 'EM DOWN!**

"ONE MORE MINUTE, JUDGE, AND I'D NEVER HAVE MADE IT...I TOOK OFF FROM THERE, LIKE A BAT OUT OF HELL..."

"EVEN IN THE AIR I WASN'T SAFE...LIKE *MANIACS* THEY TRIED TO CLAW INTO THE COCKPIT..."

"...UNTIL I TOOK HER UP TO *MACH TWO* AND THEN, *IT WAS ALL OVER.* "

THAT'S QUITE A STORY, RED!

SIR, THE PLAGUE HAS NOW BEEN IDENTIFIED AS VIRUS STRAIN 2T (FRU)T. THOSE POOR DEVILS MUST HAVE TWISTED THE NAME INTO THEIR STRANGE *BATTLE CRY.*

UNFORTUNATELY, BECAUSE RED CAME IN CONTACT WITH THE PLAGUE MEN, WE'VE HAD TO KEEP HIM HERE...

...IN CASE HE'S ONE OF THE TEN PER CENT THE VACCINE *DOESN'T WORK ON!*

BUT MY TIME'S ALMOST UP. IF I DON'T SHOW ANY SYMPTOMS WITHIN THE NEXT HOUR, *I CAN GO HOME.*

THAT'S REAL *GOOD NEWS,* RED.

ONLY *ONE* SECTION OF MEGA-CITY TWO IS HOLDING OUT. IT DESPERATELY NEEDS THAT VACCINE.

WITH THE AIRPORTS IN THE PLAGUE MEN'S HANDS, THERE'S ONLY *ONE* OTHER WAY...

...*BY LAND!* AND THAT'S WHERE I COME IN, HUH?

FORGET IT! TO SURVIVE *THE CURSED EARTH*, A THOUSAND MILES OF MAN-MADE HELL, I'D NEED *SPECIAL* MEN...A *SPECIAL* MACHINE...

WE GOT THEM, DREDD...IF *YOU'LL* DO IT...

HUUUH...? MY HANDS...? *WHAT'S* HAPPENING...?

TOOTY...?

YOUR SURVIVAL CHANCES ARE *LOW*...BUT IT'S *GOT* TO BE TRIED...

...*FOR THE FUTURE* OF CIVILISATION..!

...IS IN YOUR HANDS! *AAAGH!*

TOOTY FRUITY!

HE'S STRANGLING HIM... HE'S TURNED INTO A PLAGUE MAN!

HE-HE'S *SHOVING* THE ASSISTANT GRAND JUDGE THROUGH HIS *FOOD STERILISATION CHAMBER!*

WANT... *MUST HAVE...* FORBIDDEN FRUIT!

MUST HAVE!

STAND BACK, DREDD. *THERE'S NO REASONING WITH HIM*...I'LL *BLAST* THE GOOK TO KINGDOM COME!

NO! IF YOU BURST THAT BUBBLE, THE DISEASE WILL *SPREAD* INTO THE MEGA-CITY! I'LL HANDLE THIS.

FOOD STERILE UNIT

DROKK! THE BUBBLE'S PULLING MY PUNCHES!

RED NOT LIKE THAT, DREDD... RED MAKE YUM-YUM WITH YOU...!

...RED...WANT...YOUR JUICES!

RED... YOU GOTTA UNDERSTAND... I WANT TO HELP YOU...

UUHH!

OH, NO! HE'S GRABBING JUDGE FODDER'S GUN!

HA! RED BLAST HIS WAY OUT!

IF HE PULLS THAT TRIGGER, HE'LL BLOW HIMSELF AND HIS GERMS ALL OVER MEGA-CITY!

EVERY JUDGES' GUN HAS A SELF-DESTRUCT MECHANISM IF USED BY UNAUTHORISED PERSONS...

TOOTY FRUITY!

ONLY ONE CHANCE... THE T.V...

YOU HAD TO KILL THE PLAGUE MEN...AND NOW— I GOTTA KILL YOU!

I'M SORRY, OLD BUDDY—THERE'S NO OTHER WAY.

AAAGH!

HE'S DEAD! YOU JUST SAVED MEGA-CITY ONE, DREDD. NOW... WILL YOU SAVE MEGA-CITY TWO?

WHEN THOUSANDS COULD TURN INTO CRAZY MONSTERS LIKE RED...? THERE'S NO REFUSING!

I OWE HIM! ...SHOW ME MY WHEELS...I WANT TO GET MOVING... FAST!

SOMEHOW I'M GONNA MAKE IT — ACROSS THE CURSED EARTH!

Next Prog: INTO THE DARKNESS!

THE CURSED EARTH. CHAPTER 3:

THE DEVIL'S LAPDOGS

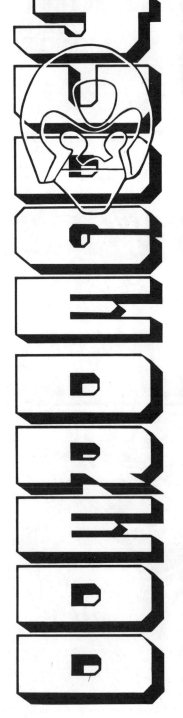

THE CURSED EARTH
CHAPTER 4.

THE TOWN OF DELIVERANCE, IN THE CURSED EARTH, IS IN TROUBLE... *BIG TROUBLE!* IT IS BEING ATTACKED BY A RAIN OF FLYING RATS—AND JUST ONE BITE FROM THE RATS IS... *CERTAIN DEATH!*

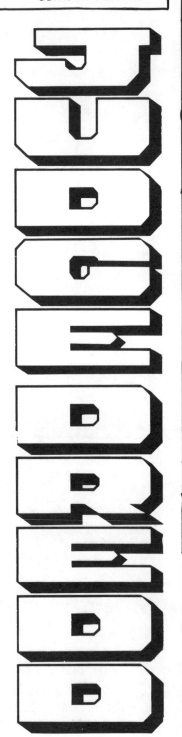

SECONDS TICKED BY, THEN...

ITS FUR'S ON END... *LEAPING FOR MY FACE!* GOTTA —

— GRAB ITS THROAT AND... *SQUEEZE THE ...LIFE OUT...OF IT!*

THE FINAL BATTLE OVER, DREDD AND SPIKES DROVE BACK INTO DELIVERANCE.

YOU HAVEN'T SEEN THE *LAST* OF THE RATS...BUT *IF* YOU ERECT SIRENS WELL AWAY FROM THE TOWN, IT'LL *LURE* THEM AWAY.

THEN YOU'LL HAVE ENOUGH FOOD TO EAT — SO MAYBE YOU CAN GO IN FOR MORE CIVILISED LAWS IN FUTURE, HUH?

YES, NOW THE LAWGIVER IS *DEAD,* THINGS WILL *CHANGE* AROUND HERE. WE ARE IN YOUR DEBT, JUDGE.

AS DREDD AND SPIKES DROVE BACK TO THE WAITING LAND-RAIDER...

YOU KNOW, JUDGEY— THE REASON I DELAYED RESCUING YOU WAS 'COS I WAS LOOKING ROUND DELIVERANCE... CAME ACROSS A *COUPLE OF INTERESTING ITEMS.*

WHEN WE GET INSIDE, I'LL SHOW YOU...

I CAN *HARDLY WAIT!*

GENUINE WORLD WAR TWO *HAND GRENADES* AND A *COLT SIX SHOOTER.* HOW D'YOU LIKE ME? D'YOU THINK I LOOK CUTE...LIKE ONE OF DEM TWENTIETH CENTURY *PUNK ROCKERS?*

YOU—ER—LOOK *WONDERFUL,* SPIKES!

AS THE LAND-RAIDER CONTINUED ITS PERILOUS JOURNEY...

BACK TO BUSINESS, GENTLEMEN... WE'VE OVERCOME THE DEVIL'S LAPDOGS — BUT EVEN *WORSE* DANGERS AWAIT US. WE HAVEN'T MET *THE MUTIES, THE WHIPPER-SNAPPERS,* OR *THE SLAY-RIDERS.... YET!*

NEXT PROG:
THE MUTIE MOUNTAINS!

THE MUTANT SPED BACK TOWARDS THE CITY...

HO! HO!

IN A SUPERMARKET IN THE RUINED CITY... BROTHER MORGAR, LEADER OF THE BROTHERHOOD OF DARKNESS...

BROTHERS *OBEE* AND *JOBEE*... TASTE THIS FOOD THAT HAS BEEN DISCOVERED — TO MAKE SURE IT WILL NOT *POISON* YOUR LEADER...

≡MMMM≡ *BAKED BEANS* — VINTAGE TWENTIETH CENTURY... A RARE AND JUICY DELICACY, *BROTHER MORGAR*.

IS GOOD... VERY GOOD...

ALL RIGHT, *THAT'S ENOUGH*... YOU'RE JUST MEANT TO *TASTE* IT!

AH, BROTHER GOMORRAH, WHAT *NEWS* DO YOU BRING US?

AFTER THE MUTANT HAD EXPLAINED...

SO... A PARTY OF *NORMS* CROSSING OUR *SACRED MOUNTAINS*... DEFILING THEM! REMEMBER, O MY BROTHERS, THE *VOW* WE MADE ON THE DAY WE *CRAWLED OUT* FROM THE FALL OUT... ALL NORMS MUST DIE! *THEY MUST NOT ESCAPE!*

MEANWHILE...

THE CANNON'S *BLASTING* A WAY UP THE MOUNTAIN... BUT THERE'S ONLY OLD *TOURIST PATHS* PAST THE FACES OF THE PRESIDENTS... THEY CAN'T TAKE A BATTLE WAGON *LIKE THIS*!

WE'LL SEE. *I'LL RIDE SHOTGUN.* HOLD HER *STEADY*, JUDGE GRADGRIND

SUDDENLY...

DEATH TO THE NORMS!

AAAHZZZzz.

DREDD! THAT THING... IT'S SLASHED RIGHT THROUGH THE ROOF!

THE MUTANTS HAVE GOT A "LA-SAW" MOBILE....! THE MACHINE 21st CENTURY SCULPTORS USED TO CARVE PRESIDENT CARTER'S FACE.

FULL SPEED... ACTIVATE ALL GUNS!

DAT MUST BE HOW DA MUTIES MADE THE FACE OF THEIR LEADER! AND NOW THEY'RE GONNA DO SOME MORE CARVING...

...ON US!

AIEEEE! LET DARKNESS TRIUMPH OVER LIGHT!

"OUR SHELLS HAVE NO EFFECT ON THOSE LASER BLADES! THEY'LL CUT US TO BITS..."

THANK YOU, JUDGE GRADGRIND...

DREDD TO BOTH MODULE COMMANDERS... ADOPT SEPARATION PROCEDURE... READY TO ACTIVATE...

...NOW!

THE KILLDOZER SLAMMED ON ITS BRAKES, AND THE RAIDER CAR DISENGAGED AND LEAPED FORWARD.

BY STOMM! WE DID IT—BUT THE ROAD'S SMASHED TO BITS...

WE CAN'T RE-DOCK WITH THE RAIDER CAR... IT'S ON ITS OWN!

AND LOOK WHAT'S HEADING TOWARDS IT!

"...DA WHOLE OF DA MUTIE BRUDDERHOOD!"

THE DAY OF ATONEMENT IS AT HAND!

YEAH—BUT RIGHT NOW—OUR FRIEND IN THAT FLYING BUZZ SAW IS COMING IN FOR THE KILL...

IF MY SLUG HITS THE LASER BLADES... WE'VE HAD IT!

GOT TO AIM PAST THEM...IN AT THE PILOT...

EEEEUGH!

THE LA-SAW SPUN CRAZILY OUT OF CONTROL...

NO! NO! NOT... THE TEETH!

AAAGH!

GOOD SHOOTING, JUDGEY!

THE RAIDER CAR—LOADED WITH THE *VITAL VACCINE*—IS STILL AT THE MUTANTS MERCY!

NO WAY WE CAN HELP THEM! *UNLESS...*

THE BOFFINS TELL US THE KILLDOZER IS CAPABLE OF *CLIMBING ANY TERRAIN*... OKAY—LET'S PUT IT TO THE *TEST...*

WE'RE GONNA CLIMB—*THE HEIGHTS OF ABRAHAM!*

SO...

COME ON...THE KILLDOZER'S STARTING TO SLIP...PUT HER IN A *LOWER GEAR!*

BUT, JUDGE... SHE'S IN *BOTTOM GEAR* ALREADY!

KEEP *ROOTING* FOR US, *ABE* BABY!

MEANWHILE... THE NORMS HAVE *SURRENDERED,* BROTHER MORGAR. THEY REALISED THEY WERE *POWERLESS* TO RESIST!

IT IS WELL DONE. A MUTIE ALWAYS GETS HIS MAN.

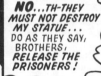

THE CURSED EARTH CHAPTER 6.
DARK AUTUMN!

JUDGE DREDD

THE LAND-RAIDER — WITH JUDGE DREDD AND HIS SPECIAL COMBAT TEAM — CONTINUES ITS JOURNEY TOWARDS MEGA-CITY TWO, ACROSS THE CURSED EARTH — THE STRETCH OF DESERT LEFT OVER FROM THE ATOMIC WARS . . .

THE BROTHERHOOD ARE STILL ON OUR TRACKS, BUT THE LAND-RAIDER IS EQUIPPED WITH ALL THE LATEST WAR WEAPONS, JUDGE DREDD.

ONE WAY

2000 A.D.
Credit Card:

SCRIPT ROBOT
PAT MILLS

ART ROBOT
MIKE McMAHON

LETTERING ROBOT
TOM FRAME

COMPU-73E

THE CURSED EARTH
CHAPTER 8.
THE SLEEPER AWAKES!

JUDGE DREDD

ON THE WILD HILLBILLY TERRITORY OF KENTUCKY, A STRANGE VAMPIRE HAS BEEN ATTACKING AND DRAINING ITS VICTIMS OF THEIR LIFE BLOOD.

THE HILLBILLIES APPEAL TO JUDGE DREDD FOR HELP, AND A SEARCH LEADS TO THE VAULTS OF RUINED FORT KNOX, WHERE . . .

IN THE VAULT...

THIS BE THE VAMPIRE...

...GOTTA RAM THE STAKE RIGHT THROUGH ITS BLACK HEART!

DROKK IT! THE HILLBILLIES ARE GOING TO KILL...

THE LAST PRESIDENT OF THE UNITED STATES!

WE ARE VERY SORRY.

IF THERE'S ANYWAY WE CAN MAKE AMENDS...

JUST STOP TALKING IN THAT TRIPLE ECHO... IT'S DRIVING ME NUTS! YOU'RE WORSE THAN THAT METAL FREAK I LEFT BEHIND IN MEGA-CITY ONE!

OKAY — BUT I WISH I KNEW WHAT WAS GOING ON!

YOU'LL FIND OUT SOON ENOUGH, SPIKES! I ONLY HOPE WE'RE IN TIME!

COME ON, SPIKES!

MEANWHILE...

ANOTHER BASH WITH THE MALLET SHOULD DO IT, IKKABOD! IT'S THE ONLY WAY!

"AAAH! THE VAMPIRE'S WAKING UP!"

QUICK...DRIVE THE STAKE HOME — BEFORE THE CREATURE DESTROYS US ALL!

DROKK IT! THEY'VE STOPPED THE CRYOGENIC PROCESS... HOLD IT RIGHT THERE!

SHOULDN'T HAVE DONE THAT, JUDGE... THE VAMPIRE OWES US — FOR WHAT HE DID TO OUR FOLK!

STAND IN OUR WAY AGAIN, AND —

NO! THERE'S BEEN ENOUGH BLOODSHED...THE MAN YOU'RE ABOUT TO KILL IS *ROBERT L. BOOTH* — *LAST PRESIDENT OF THE UNITED STATES!*

WHAT?

YOU WANT AN EXPLANATION? *OKAY, YOU GOT IT!* NOW LISTEN... AND LISTEN GOOD...

"WE'VE GOT TO GO BACK *THIRTY YEARS*... TO 2070...WHEN PRESIDENT BOB BOOTH PRESSED THE BUTTON AND THE *ATOMIC WARS* BEGAN... *MILLIONS* DIED AND — OUTSIDE THE WHITE HOUSE..."

AN *END* TO *SMOOTH BOOTH!*

RESIGN! RESIGN!

WE WANT THE *JUDGES!*

POWER TO THE *JUDGES!*

"*THE JUDGES!* GENETICALLY CHOSEN TO BE *TOUGH* — BUT *FAIR*. THE PEOPLE *TURNED* TO THEM IN THE *HOUR* OF *NEED*. AND SO..."

WE'VE *COME* FOR YOU, BOOTH!

HERE IS THE *DECLARATION* OF JUDGEMENT...FOR CRIMES *AGAINST* THE AMERICAN PEOPLE, YOUR PRESIDENCY IS AT AN *END*...

WE, THE JUDGES, *HAVE TAKEN OVER!*

"PRESIDENT BOOTH WAS *TRIED* BEFORE A *GRAND COUNCIL* OF *JUDGES* AND FOUND *GUILTY* OF WAR CRIMES..."

"BUT..."

WHAT SHALL HIS SENTENCE BE? AMERICA IS IN *RUINS*... HE *CANNOT* BE ALLOWED TO LIVE...

BUT HE CANNOT BE *ALLOWED TO DIE!* WE CANNOT EXECUTE THE LAST PRESIDENT OF THE UNITED STATES!

"ONLY THE JUDGES COULD COME UP WITH A SENTENCE THAT WAS *FAIR*... THE FAMOUS "*JUDGEMENT OF SOLOMON*"!

MR. PRESIDENT, WE SENTENCE YOU TO... *ONE HUNDRED YEARS SUSPENDED ANIMATION!*

YOU WILL BE TAKEN FROM HERE TO *FORT KNOX* — FOR PROTECTION — AND *THERE*, YOUR BODY FROZEN AND STORED IN THE DEEPEST VAULT!

"AT FORT KNOX — THREE MEDIC ROBOTS — *SPECIALLY PROGRAMMED*, LOOKED AFTER THE PRESIDENT..."

"YEAR AFTER YEAR...THEY FAITHFULLY CHECKED AND *CHANGED* HIS BLOOD..."

"UNTIL THE DAY A BOMB HIT FORT KNOX — AND ONLY THE PRESIDENT AND THE ROBOTS WERE LEFT ALIVE..."

THERE'S NO MORE BLOOD. BUT WE MUST OBEY OUR PROGRAMMING....

WE MUST *SEARCH* FOR...

...*MORE!*

THAT'S HOW THE *LEGEND* OF THE *VAMPIRE* GREW IN THESE PARTS...

ROBOTS WHO WERE TRYING TO KEEP THEIR PRESIDENT *ALIVE* — THE *ONLY* WAY THEY KNEW HOW. COME AND MEET... "*SNAP*", "*CRACKLE*" AND "*POP*"!

DREDD LED THEM TO THE FLOOR ABOVE...

I'M AFRAID IT'S *TRUE.* WE...

...DID GO AROUND "*DRINKING*" EVERYONE'S MOTION LOTION.

AND WE'D LIKE TO APOLOGISE!

SO *YOU* BE THE ONE'S WHO *KILLED* MY DAUGHTER!

WAIT! THAT WON'T BRING HER BACK, IKKABOD...BUT "*SNAP*", "*CRACKLE*" AND "*POP*" CAN BE *MENDED* AND *REPROGRAMMED* TO *WORK FOR YOU*... THAT MAKES A LOT MORE *SENSE!*

THE JUDGE IS *RIGHT*... THERE'S BEEN *ENOUGH* FEUDIN'...

THE CURSED
EARTH
CHAPTER 9.

THE SLAY-RIDERS!

JUDGE DREDD

JUDGE'S LOG . . . . DAY TWELVE
JOURNEY CO-ORDINATES A7..L5..3.
TODAY WE CROSS THE MISSISSIPPI,
CONTINUING OUR JOURNEY TO MEGA-CITY TWO.
THE ONCE MIGHTY RIVER IS STILL ABLAZE
WITH PETROL, FOUL-SMELLING
POLLUTANTS, AND NUCLEAR WASTES FROM
THE DAYS OF THE GREAT ATOMIC WAR.
IT HAS BECOME — A TORRENT
OF FIERY DEATH !

AS THE LAND RAIDER REACHED THE OTHER SIDE AND LOADED UP WITH PROVISIONS...

SURE IS GOOD TO SEE SOME *HUMAN* FACES AGAIN... SPECIALLY A *MEGA-CITY LAWMAN* LIKE YOURSELF, JUDGE DREDD. WE'VE HEARD OF YOU — *EVEN* IN THESE PARTS.

THAT *IS* HOW IT SHOULD BE, FERRY-MASTER. BUT *HOW* DID YOU COME BY ALL THESE ALIENS?

SPECIMENS BROUGHT BACK BY THE STARSHIPS...USED TO BE KEPT ON AN *ALIEN NATURE RESERVE* NEAR HERE...

BUT THEN THE WAR CAME AND *EVERYTHING* CHANGED, ME AND SOME OF THE OTHER LOCALS *BOUGHT 'EM UP CHEAP.*

AND USED THEM AS *SLAVE LABOUR.* YOUR TRADE *SICKENS* ME TO MY GUTS, FERRY-MASTER.

NOW —ER— DON'T START FEELING *SORRY* FOR 'EM, JUDGE. THEY *AIN'T* INTELLIGENT.

SEE THAT FURRY ONE... *HE EATS ROCKS!* CAN YOU THINK OF *ANYTHING DUMBER?*

SHEESH, JUDGEY... I'D HAVE A *HELLUVA* BELLY-ACHE IF I EAT GRANITE STEAKS LIKE *FREAK-FACE.*

HAW, HAW! THE STUPID BEAST'S REAL *CHEAP* TO FEED... I GIVE 'IM A COUPLE O' BOULDERS A DAY AN' HE WORKS *HARDER* THAN A GANG OF ROBO-NAVVIES.

MAYBE HE FINDS THE WAY HUMANS EAT OTHER ANIMALS *JUST AS STUPID.*

SUDDENLY...

LOOK OUT, JUDGE —THE BRUTE CAN *CRACK YOUR SKULL IN HALF* WITH THOSE PINCERS!

TWURP!

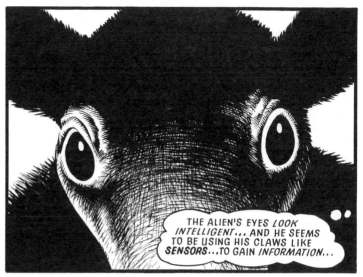

NEXT PROG: REQUIEM FOR AN ALIEN !

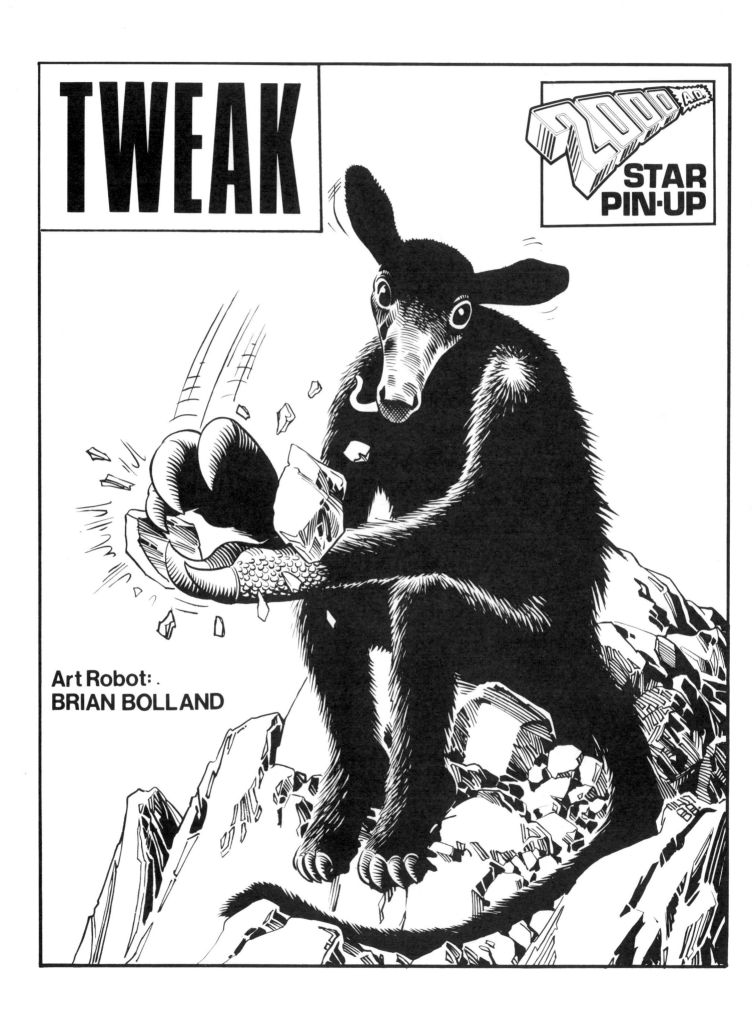

TWEAK, AIN'T MUCH I CAN DO TO MAKE AMENDS, BUDDY...BUT YOU'RE WELCOME TO COME WITH US. AND — I'M SORRY.

FILL IN THE GRAVE!

TWOLK!

WH-WHAT WAS IN THE GRAVE?

THREE ALIENS — LIKE TWEAK, TWO OF THEM SMALL — AND THE OTHER WITH GOLDEN FUR... YEAH, TWEAK'S MATE AND KIDS...SHOT — BY HUMAN BULLETS!

THAT'S WHY TWEAK ESCAPED — SO HE COULD REACH THIS PLANTATION WHERE THEY WERE SLAVES — SO HE COULD SEE HIS FAMILY AGAIN...

MY GUESS IS THE PLANTATION OWNER — ONE OF THE SLAY-RIDERS — FOUND THEY DIDN'T WORK HARD ENOUGH — AND HAD THEM SHOT...

SO TWEAK BURIED THEM AND BEGAN LAYING ROCKS ON THEIR GRAVE..."FOOD" FOR THEIR JOURNEY AFTER DEATH — ACCORDING TO THE CUSTOM ON HIS PLANET... AND WE'RE GONNA HELP HIM...!

AND SO...

TWURRRRP!

I THINK TWEAK'S TRYING TO TELL YOU, SPIKES — HE ONLY LIKES THE HARD STUFF... GRANITE AND QUARTZ!

SHEESH! HE'S REALLY FUSSY ABOUT HIS GRUB — AND I LUGGED THESE NICE JUICY ROCKS ALL THE WAY UP THE HILL SPECIAL.

THEY LEFT TWEAK ALONE FOR A FEW MINUTES BY THE GRAVE...

DRAGGED AS A SPECIMEN OFF HIS HOME PLANET... SOLD INTO SLAVERY...HIS MATE AND KIDS BUTCHERED ON A WORLD LIGHT YEARS AWAY FROM HOME... YEAH, TWEAK MUST REALLY THINK WE HUMANS ARE CIVILISED!

THE LAND-RAIDER CONTINUED ITS DANGEROUS JOURNEY TO MEGA-CITY TWO, ACROSS THE CURSED EARTH...

JUDGE DREDD'S LOG: DAY THIRTEEN JOURNEY CO-ORDINATES: A9-L6.8.

SOMETIMES THE HUMAN RACE MAKES ME SICK!

JUDGE DREDD WILL RETURN IN PART 2 OF THE CURSED EARTH.

THE CURSED EARTH
CHAPTER 11
THE COMING OF SATANUS!

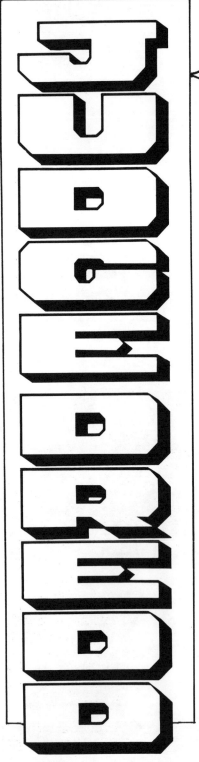

THE BEASTS THUNDERED FORWARD, THEIR HEARTS BEATING WITH **FEAR**. THEY HAD SMELT THE SCENT OF THE **DARK ONE**, EVEN BEFORE THEY HAD SEEN HIM, AND **PANIC** HAD SPREAD THROUGH THEM LIKE WILDFIRE...

BY STOMM!

THEY HEARD THE DARK ONE'S EVIL SQUAWKING BEHIND THEM...HEARD ITS BESTIAL SCREECH OF GLEE AS IT DRAGGED ONE OF THEM, SCREAMING WITH TERROR, TO THE GROUND. THEY MUST KEEP RUNNING! **RUNNING!**

JUDGE DREDD TO CREW... BATTLE STATIONS!

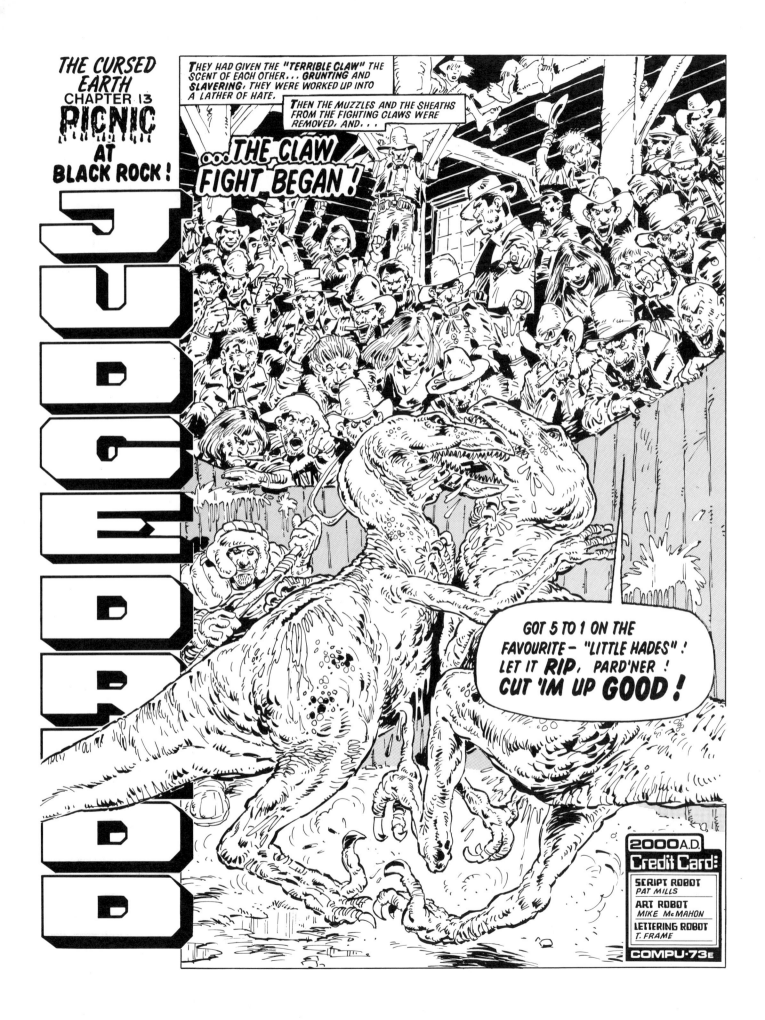

SUDDENLY —

TWURRRK!

BY STOMM! IT'S TWEAK!

WHADDAYAKNOW... THAT DUMB *FUR RUG* CAME GOOD!

WELL DONE, TWEAK...*SPIKES*, PREPARE THE KILL-DOZER! *ACTIVATE THE ROBOTS!* ISSUE THEM WITH FLAME THROWERS AND PROGRAM THEM FOR NO.3 — "RIOT AND HEAVY DUTY ASSAULT WORK!"

I'M ONLY GOING TO ASK YOU ONCE... JUDGE JACK! *WHERE?*

I-IN...THE JAILHOUSE... HE-HE'S IN THE NEXT BATCH TO BE *SACRIFICED* TO HIS SATANIC MAJESTY!

BUT AT THAT MOMENT, INSANE RED EYES WERE ALREADY GLARING INTO THE JAILHOUSE...

THE DARK ONE HAD FOLLOWED THE SCENT INTO TOWN AND — *THERE WAS A LOT OF WORK TO BE DONE HERE . . .*

TEN TONS OF TERROR SMASHED INTO THE JAIL!

AAAAGH!

SATANUS HAD GONE ALONG WITH "THE ARRANGEMENT" IN THE PAST — *THE BELLS, THE ROCK, THE HUMAN SACRIFICES,* ALL THAT BIT... BUT HE *NEEDED* NOW!

HE CRAMMED AS MANY AS HE COULD INTO HIS MAW, BUT COULDN'T GET THE OTHERS IN — JUST FOR THE MOMENT —

MERCY! MERCY!

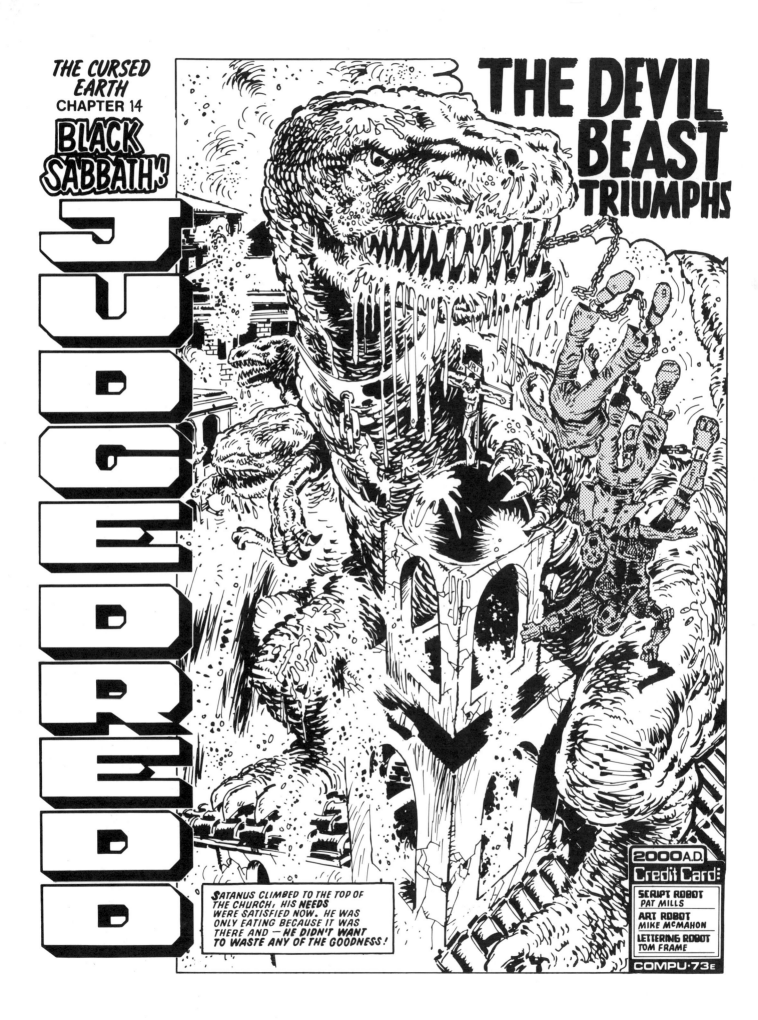

THE CURSED EARTH CHAPTER 14

BLACK SABBATH'S JUDGE DREDD

THE DEVIL BEAST TRIUMPHS

SATANUS CLIMBED TO THE TOP OF THE CHURCH, HIS NEEDS WERE SATISFIED NOW. HE WAS ONLY EATING BECAUSE IT WAS THERE AND — HE DIDN'T WANT TO WASTE ANY OF THE GOODNESS!

2000 A.D.
Credit Card:

SCRIPT ROBOT
PAT MILLS

ART ROBOT
MIKE McMAHON

LETTERING ROBOT
TOM FRAME

COMPU·73E

COVERED IN FLAMES, HIS HOWLS WERE **HORRIBLE** TO HEAR. SO MUCH HE **STILL** HAD TO DO —

GIVE IT — **WHITE HEAT!**

ONE LAST **HIDEOUS SCREAM** SCREECHED FROM THE TORMENTED ANIMAL. *THE SCREAM OF A CREATURE WHO SHOULD NEVER HAVE BEEN BORN...*

...A CREATURE OUT OF TIME! ...THEN **SILENCE!**

IT IS — OVER!

OVER...FER... **YOU TOO, DREDD!**

YOU...TURNED THE FORCES OF DARKNESS **AGAINST** REPENTANCE... I TRIED TO TELL THEM *I* WAS ON THEIR SIDE — BUT...WOULDN'T LISTEN...TURNED ON ME...

"BULL CANNON...HE'S GOT A TYRANNOSAUR'S **TOOTH** IN HIS HEAD..."

THE DYING BLACKSMITH RIPPED THE MUZZLE OFF HIS GHASTLY PET —

KILL!

LITTLE HADES — THE COCKY WINNER OF A HUNDRED CLAW FIGHTS — SPRANG INTO ACTION...

THEN... **TWAARK!**

*THE FURRY ALIEN WAS DESPERATE TO **SAVE** HIS FRIEND. LITTLE HADES MIGHT BE A VICIOUS FIGHTER —*

— BUT TWEAK'S CLAWS COULD BREAK BOULDERS IN HALF IN SECONDS!

NO CONTEST!

THANKS, TWEAK!

THIS TOWN IS FINISHED NOW. JUST A SMOULDERING RUIN. LET'S MOVE OUT!

DREDD SPOKE TO THE PEOPLE OF REPENTANCE —

GO! INTO THE CURSED EARTH... AND, IF YOU EVER RETURN TO YOUR EVIL WAYS, BE SURE THE LAW WILL TRACK YOU DOWN... PUNISH YOU! AND I AM THE LAW!

LONG AFTER DREDD HAD GONE... OUT OF THE CRYPT... A SMOULDERING BLACK SHAPE WAS EMERGING...

SATANUS!

HE HAD ESCAPED — BY CRASHING THROUGH THE FLOOR OF THE RUINED CHURCH... INTO THE VAULT BELOW!

NOW THE MONSTER FROM THE UNDEAD NEEDED TO HOLE UP FOR A WHILE. LICK HIS GRISLY WOUNDS... THEN — LOOK FOR MORE WORK!

IT HAD BEEN GOOD — WHILE IT LASTED. HE WAS NOT AS GREAT AS HIS MOTHER... BUT HE'D MADE A START... AND — THE AWFUL THING HE WAS GOING TO DO IN THE FUTURE WOULD MAKE HIM — EVEN GREATER!

YES, HE'D BE BACK... THE WORLD HAD NOT SEEN THE LAST OF THE SON OF OLD ONE EYE... SATANUS THE UNCHAINED!

NEXT PROG: LOSER'S LEAP!

THE WINNER, DREDD RETURNED TO VEGAS HALL OF JUSTICE, WHICH HAD BEEN TURNED INTO A CASINO BY THE MAFIA JUDGES—BUT—

YOU EXPECT US TO TAKE ORDERS FROM YOU? THAT'S **DEAD MAN'S** THINKING!

I DON'T. BUT **THEY** DO— LOOK!

DA **LEAGUE AGAINST GAMBLIN'** CREEPS! HUNDREDS OF DEM!

GET THOSE UNIFORMS OFF. YOU'RE NOT **FIT** TO WEAR THEM!

YOU HEARD THE **JUDGE!**

OKAY! OKAY!

THE LEAGUE AGAINST GAMBLING WAS GOOD ENOUGH TO HANDLE THESE MAFIA RATS. ALL THEY NEEDED WAS SOMEONE TO LEAD THEM!

THEN—

ONE OF THE GUYS FOUND THIS GOD-JUDGE GEAR, DREDD!

...HE WILL TAKE UNTO HIM SACRED ROBES, AND IN ALL THE CITY HIS NAME WILL BE **DREAD!**

I'M ALREADY A JUDGE OF MEGA-CITY 1, RUDY—YOU WEAR THE GEAR! THE LEAGUE AGAINST GAMBLING HAS SHOWN LAS VEGAS THE WAY TO SANITY. NOW YOU MUST FINISH THE JOB YOURSELVES!

AND SO DREDD ONCE MORE GUNNED THE LAND-RAIDER TOWARD THE OBJECT OF HIS MERCY MISSION— MEGA-CITY 2...

I-I DON'T UNDERSTAND. THE SAVIOUR WAS **SUPPOSED** TO REMAIN ONE SCORE YEARS AND FOUR!

HIS MEMORY WILL, LINUS—NO-ONE'S GOING TO FORGET THE DAY JUDGE DREDD CAME TO VEGAS— **AND WON!**

NEXT PROG: **TWEAK'S STORY!**

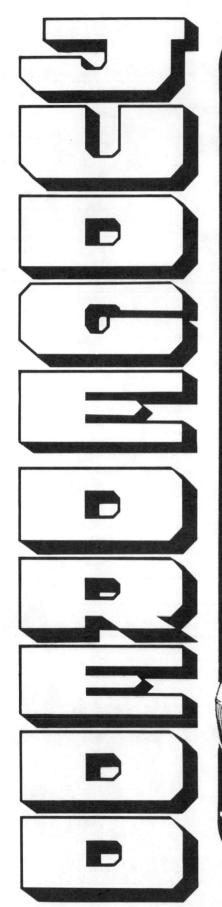

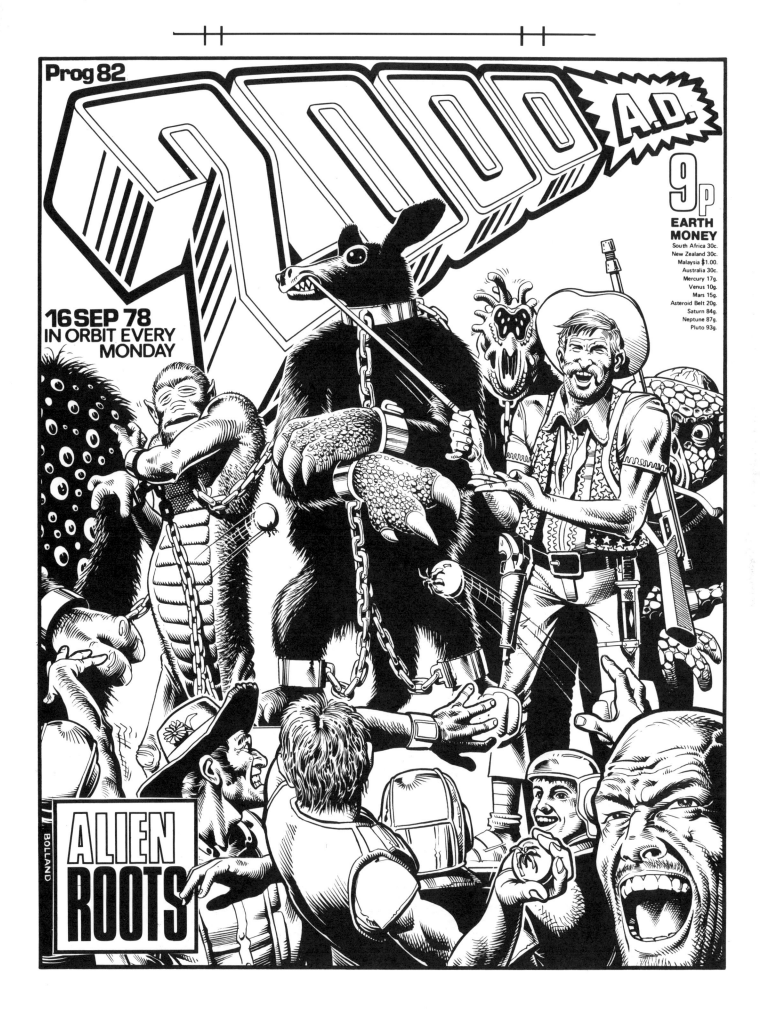

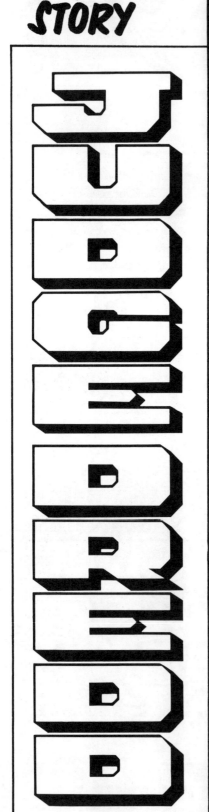

THE CURSED EARTH
CHAPTER 17
TWEAK'S STORY

TAKE HIM DOWN.

IF THE HUMANS KNEW THE TRUTH—THEY WOULD RETURN TO HIS PLANET. DISCOVER THE UNDERGROUND FARMS WHERE HIS PEOPLE HARVESTED GOLD, DIAMONDS AND OTHER ROCKS FOR FOOD—

THE HUMANS WOULD MINE IT AND HIS PEOPLE *STARVE*...WHILE THE HUMANS GREW RICH AS THEY SPREAD THEIR *POLLUTION* AND *DISEASES*...

GIVE HIM THE ALIEN I.Q. TESTS AGAIN.

NOW, TWEAK—THIS IS A *BOOK*. WHAT DO YOU DO WITH A *BOOK*?

ENCYCLOPEDIA EARTH

TWAAAAWK?

NO, YOU DON'T EAT IT, YOU *DUMB* ANIMAL!

TWOKK!

TWOL!

THE THICK BRUTE DOESN'T UNDERSTAND WEAPONS EITHER—HE'S POINTING THE GUN WE GAVE HIM AT HIMSELF!

HE CAN'T EVEN WALK THROUGH A DOOR! YES, I'M AFRAID HE'S DEFINITELY *STUPID!*

IN THE PLANTATION, TWEAK'S GOLDEN FURRED MATE HAD BEEN WORKING. SUDDENLY—WITH HER ALIEN POWERS OF FORESEEING THE FUTURE—SHE KNEW WHAT WAS GOING TO HAPPEN—

TWAAAAR!

DESPERATELY RAN TO THEIR AID—

SO YOU WANT SOME TOO, HUH?

TRIED TO TAKE THE BULLETS FOR THEM—

TWEAK! TWEAK! TWEAK!

BUT—AS SHE DIED...

AAAGGGH!

MEANWHILE, TWEAK—DESPERATE TO BE REUNITED WITH HIS FAMILY—HAD ESCAPED... ONLY TO FIND THEM—TOO LATE...

TWAAAAAW!

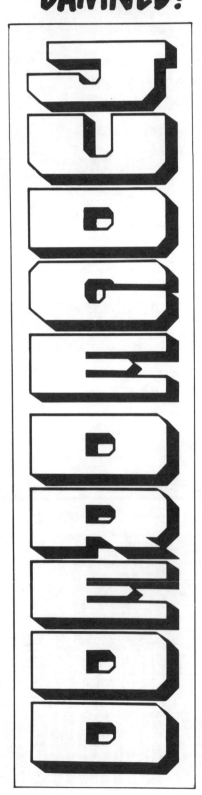